D1072586

creatures great and small . . .

MICHAEL FLANDERS
MARCELLO MINALE

CREATURES GREAT AND SMALL.....

HOLT, RINEHART AND WINSTON   NEW YORK / CHICAGO / SAN FRANCISCO

The Brontosaurus
Had a brain
No bigger than
A crisp;

The Dodo
Had a stammer
And the Mammoth
Had a lisp;

The Auk
Was just too Aukward —
Now they're none of them
Alive.

Each one,
(Like Man),
Had shown himself
Unfitted to survive.

This story
Points a moral:
Now it's
We
Who wear the pants;

The extinction
Of these species
Holds a lesson
For us
ANTS.

THE ELEPHANT———

This African Elephant — look at his ears —
Astride the Equator we find.
A lifetime of leisure has left him, one fears,
Quite unable to make up his mind.

All African traffic has ground to a halt
While he ponders his weighty decision
And he's caused (though he'll tell you it wasn't his fault)
More than one very nasty collision.

On the crown of the road he's been standing for days
Just wondering whether to choose
To wander along to the grasslands to graze
Or back to the forest to snooze.

Irresolute creature! Your worries are slight,
Consider your Indian cousin
Who carries a howdah or works day and night
Dragging tree-trunks about by the dozen.

THE OWL————

I would not give
Two hoots to be
A Night Owl
Living in a tree
With naught to do
If I were he
But cry
"TU-WHIT TU-WHOO!"

On this the Owl
And I agree.

He does not wish
That he were me
Or in my boots,
Lived in a room
And cried
"TO WHOM?"
And not "TO-WHOO!"

He gives two hoots
Or even three —
"TU-WHIT TU-WHOO TU-WHOO!" to be
A Night Owl
Living in a tree!
He knows exactly
What to do . . .
TO WIT, TO WOO.

THE KANGAROO———

The Kangaroo and Wallaby inhabiting Australia,
In terms of evolution, can be counted as a failure.

But how convenient to have a safe and private pocket
Where you could pop the baby in and, preferably, lock it.

THE SPARROW———

O Lord, who marks the sparrow's fall
For our Tom cat to kill,
You do not raise him up again
Because he has free-will.
But though his sparrow bones must lie
With fish and errant mice
In Tom's infurnal regions —
Yet, his soul's in Sparadise.

THE WALRUS————

The Walrus lives on icy floes
And unsuspecting Eskimoes.

Don't bring your wife to Arctic Tundra
A Walrus may bob up from undra.

THE DUCK-BILLED PLATYPUS———

We call him "Duck-billed Platypus"
And mock him for his name;
He does not seem to mind it.
He feels no sense of shame
Because he does not know himself
By such a title,
He's
A "Golden, Shining Love-Bird"
In Duck-billed Platypese.

THE HIPPOPOTAMUS————

What fun	to be
A Hippo	-potamus
And weigh	a ton
From top	to bottamus

THE GIRAFFE——————

The Giraffe is tall,
Looks down on us all.

Lofty, stiff-necked.
Lip curled, erect,

With humourless eye
Looks down from on high,

Gives a curt little nod,
Says, "I'm nearer to God."

He's his own High Horse,
Can't get down, of course.

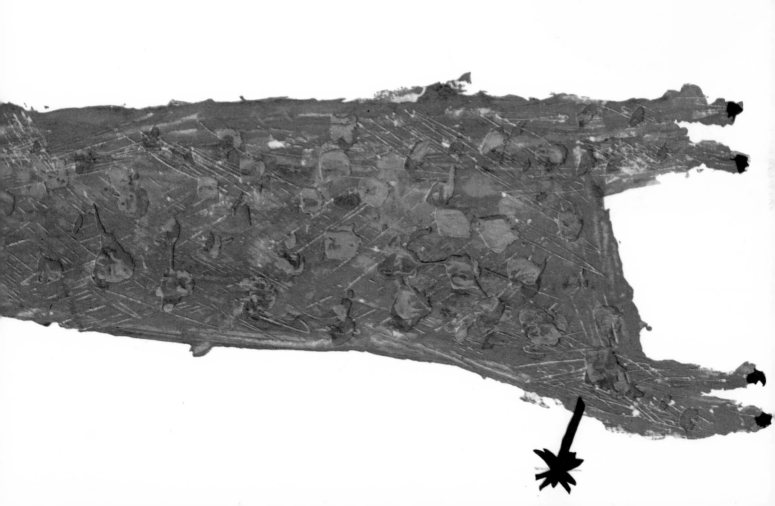

THE SNAIL———

This Snail is clamped — he knows not why —
Against some Thing . . . (a tree) ;
He does not know, "I am a Snail",
He can't imagine me.

Time has for him within his shell
No meaning and no end.
I think in many complex ways
He cannot comprehend.

Small wonder He who made my world,
Made Adam and made Eve,
Can think in many curious ways
Of which I can't conceive.

THE LION———

This Lion, to show his trust in men,
Reared a young Man child in its den.
"You see?" it said. "I win my bet.
This human is a perfect pet;
Plays with my cubs, comes when I call;
There is no vice in him at all."

Its neighbours answered, "We'll await
What happens at a later date."

The child grew up, became a Man,
Then suddenly one day began
To punch his foster-father's nose
And deal his playmates fearful blows,
He kicked and fought and scratched and bit,
He even dug a Lion Pit.

The Lion sadly murmured, "No,
This savage beast will have to go."
Gave him one last, great hunk of meat
And turned him loose in Oxford Street.

THE HUMMING BIRD————

The Humming-bird, he has no song
From flower to flower he hums along
Humming his way among the trees
He finds no words for what he sees

THE PORCUPINE———

The Porcupine (or "spiny pig")
Lurks beneath fig-trees in full fig,
That falling figs — a fruit he likes —
Impale themselves upon his spikes.
Then should he meet the fig-tree man
He'll say, "Just part of Nature's plan!"

This is a lesson to us all;
To be around, when blessings fall.

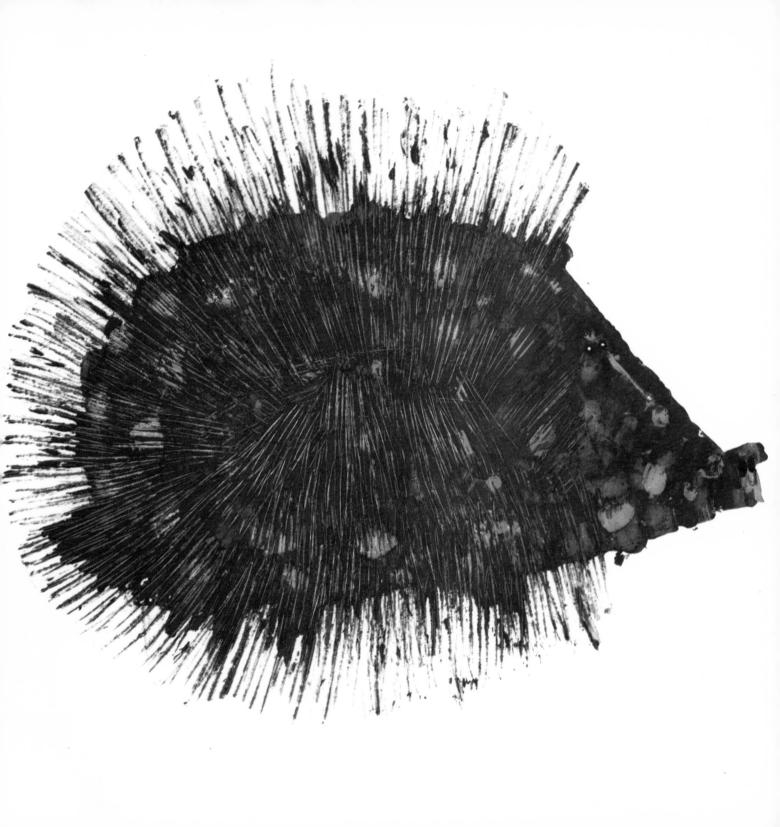

THE CAT————

Everyone's written about the Cat
From Alice to Rudyard K.
Whittington's, Lear's, the one on the mat –
They've left me nothing to say –
There's Puss-in-the-middle, the Cat and the fiddle,
Old Possum and Beatrix P.

But a Cat is a Cat
And that is that
And that's enough for me.

THE CAMEL———

Man with his hydro-electric power
Has learnt to make the desert flower,
A pleasing change to every mammal —
Except the desert-loving Camel.

He sees, with mounting irritation,
The ravages of irrigation
And water, as it flows and squirts,
Deprive him of his just desserts.

THE BAT———

The Bat has been granted a knowledge of things
Far surpassing the wisest of men;
And nightly he flutters just over our heads
And declaims it again and again.
He tells us in English, he tells us in French,
He explains it in Russian and Greek;
Revealing the ultimate meaning of life
In a wholly inaudible squeak.

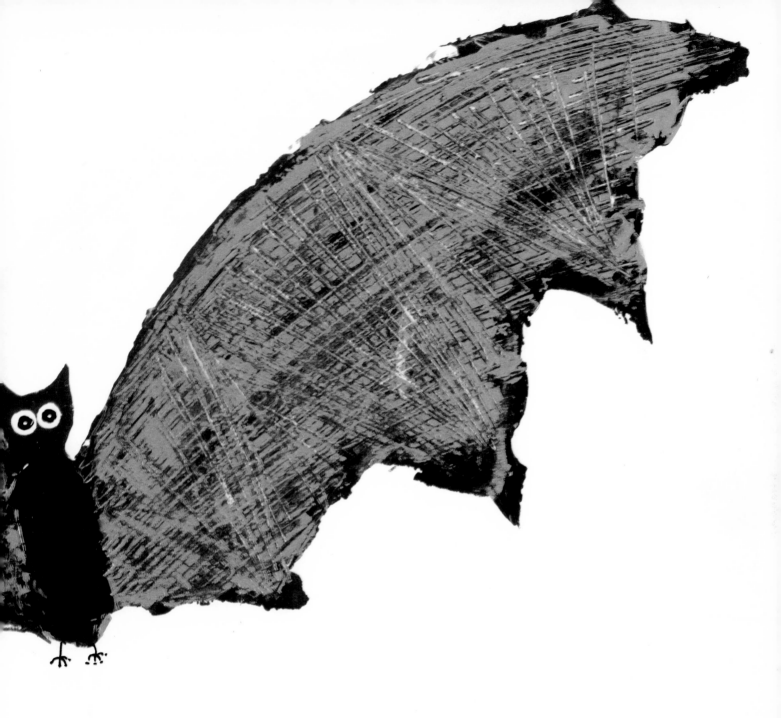

THE SHEEP———

This worried Sheep
Can't get to sleep
For counting endless files
Of phantom sheep-dogs
As they leap
Imaginary stiles.

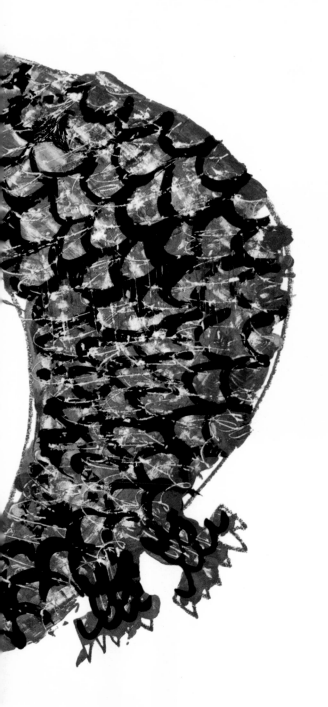

THE CROCODILE————

This is a Crocodile, my boy . . . ·
.Or is it an Alligator? . . .
I've an excellent book that you'll enjoy
We can refer to later;

The Alligator . . . no, Crocodile
Is a purplish colour beneath.
Give it a tickle to make it smile
And let's count the number of teeth,

For the Croc. (I think) has a row too few
Though the 'Gator can't wink its eye . . .

Ah!
     Now I can tell you which of the two
You have just been eaten by.

THE WOLF———

A Wolf is baying at the Moon
The Moon is beaming back . . .
O baying Wolf! Obey that beam
Before my eardrums crack!

"That Moon intends," the Wolf replies,
"To spoil my sport for spite!
It shows the shepherds where I am
By shining down so bright.

And so each night I stand at bay
With moonbeams round my head;
I'm sure the Moon goes in again
When I go back to bed!"